For Harry

A dog who loved the river.

First published in Great Britain in 2015
by Two Blondes Walking Limited
twoblondeswalking.com

Text copyright © 2015 Fi Darby
Illustrations copyright © 2015 Ali Marshall
The author and illustrator have asserted their moral rights.

ISBN 978-0-9931057-2-2 (Paperback)

Dart the River

By the Two Blondes
Illustrated by Ali Marshall

Dart the River had dozed all through the long, hot summer, but when it started to rain in October, he woke up. He woke up in a wild, lonely patch of Dartmoor blanket bog. The blanket bog was covered in wispy, yellow moor grass and beautiful green moss, but it was dark and smelly.

So Dart trickled out.

To start with, it was difficult to find a way downhill. The moor grass and the clinging moss didn't want to let him go, but Dart longed to explore, so he pushed his way downwards. Soon, other trickles, from other bogs, saw how eager Dart was, and they joined him. They didn't say anything at all.

Before long, Dart was a stream. He burbled quietly down over the moor, pouring smoothly over stones and sucking at grass roots. For ages, the only noise he could hear was Wind. Wind was wild, and always did exactly what he wanted. He whistled and shook his way past Dart. Dart wanted to chase Wind and play with him.

Dart streamed faster.

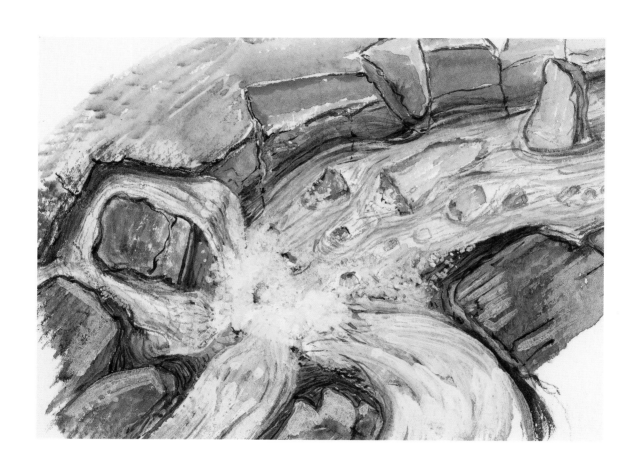

As he went on, Dart heard a different noise. It was loud, it was frightening, and it was getting nearer. Dart tried to hold back, but he was moving too quickly. The stones in the stream-bed became large, smooth rocks. Dart reached out with his fingers to try and stop himself; and then suddenly, he was flung in different directions over a waterfall. Dart was scared at first, but then it was fun; enormous, giggling fun.

Dart bounced on.

The land started to flatten. More streams joined Dart, who grew wider and rippled gently past trees and sheep. Then Dart saw the bridge in front of him. He didn't know what it was; the huge grey stones loomed above him as he slipped below them. It was cold and dark underneath, green slime grew on the stones, and there were eerie echoes. He didn't like it.

Dart hurried out.

As he emerged from the bridge, the sun broke through the cloud. There was another bridge in front of him. This ancient bridge was made of flat granite slabs, and had light shining right through it. People were standing on its smooth surface. They were dressed in bright-coloured raincoats and were taking photos of Dart. As their cameras snapped, the sunlight caught on Dart's ripples and sent rays of light all around him. Dart felt like a film star.

Dart swept past.

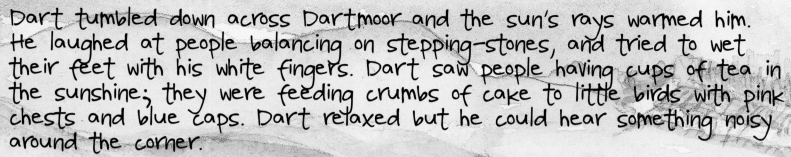

Dart tumbled down across Dartmoor and the sun's rays warmed him. He laughed at people balancing on stepping-stones, and tried to wet their feet with his white fingers. Dart saw people having cups of tea in the sunshine; they were feeding crumbs of cake to little birds with pink chests and blue caps. Dart relaxed but he could hear something noisy around the corner.

Dart babbled on.

And then suddenly, there was a rush of water on his west bank, as another river swept in next to him. Dart was unsure, this was his valley. He didn't want to share it.

"What's your name?" He sputtered, as he and the new river jostled for space.

"My name's Dart," the other river called, as he rushed away down the valley.

Dart charged after him, "But my name is Dart. Where did you come from?"

The other river laughed and splashed at Dart, "I came from the West, high on Dartmoor."

Dart was confused but there wasn't time to ask more questions; the river bed steepened, and the two rivers ran faster and faster together into a steep-sided gorge. Tumbling and whooping, the lines between them blurred. They charged over rapids and roared with laughter at each other's antics.

Dart leapt on.

By the time they reached the bottom of the gorge, Dart from the East, and Dart from the West, had merged into one bigger and cheekier Dart the river. This bigger Dart paused, next to a group of kayakers. He swirled around their boats, trying to make them fall out, but each time Dart tipped them over, the kayakers righted themselves with a flick of their long paddles. Dart liked the game but he had come to a big bend. The bend slowed him down.

Dart glided round.

What Dart saw next should have been beautiful, but it wasn't. There was a large area of bright green meadow on one bank and a high brown cliff on the other. The leaves on the trees were turning a lovely autumn brown. But people hadn't looked after this place.

They had dropped rubbish on the banks and lit fires that had burnt patches in the grass. Dart could feel broken glass as he slid over the river-bed. Dart shivered as he looked around. This place was not for him.

Dart crept on.

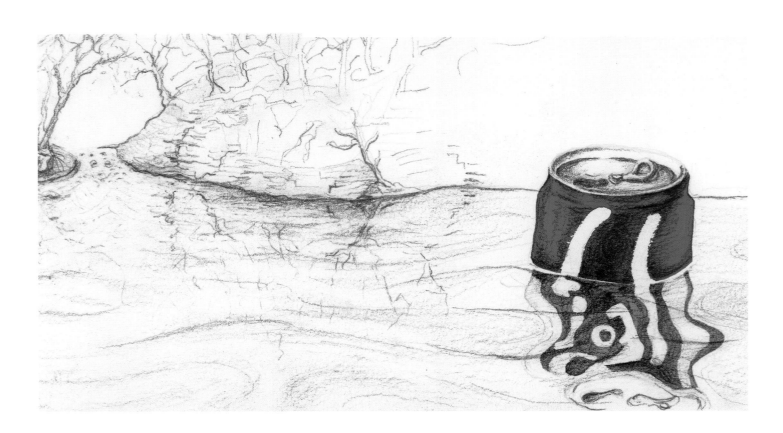

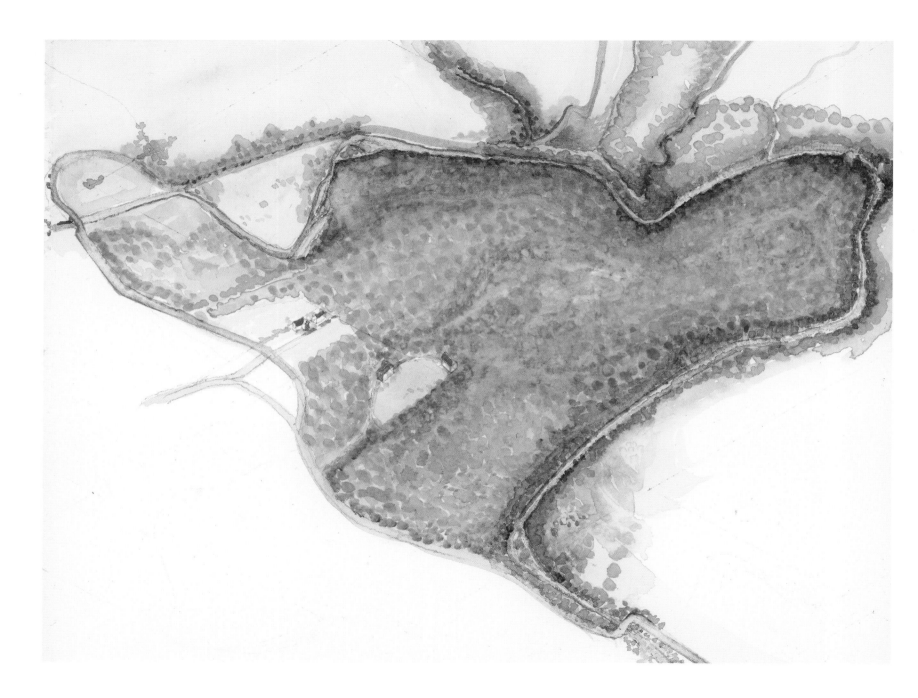

Dart wanted to get away from the strange meadow, so he moved more quickly. His route took him in a big loop, through a thickly forested valley. There were more kayakers and more rapids to play with. The valley was beautiful, but it was deep and shadowy. Dart wanted to find the sunshine again, so he kept going. As he left the valley, there were wide fields on either side of him and his banks were further apart.

Dart's mood changed; he was growing up and becoming a real river. He really wanted a boat to float along on top of him, a big boat with happy, chattering passengers. But where could he find one? Dart heard some strange noises.

"Puff, puff, whistle. Puff, puff, whistle." An odd smell hung in the chilly air.

Dart was curious. Dart was enticed on.

Dart saw the train as he swirled round another bend. It was green and gold. The noise of its wheels on the tracks was a merry one. Dart was fascinated by the passengers waving out of the train's windows. He was a bit jealous and rushed faster to keep up.

"Excuse me, excuse me!" Dart splashed, but the train didn't hear him and rattled on. Dart tried harder, he threw himself round the next bend, chucking water up onto the train track. "Excuse me!" The train heard him. "Well, you're a lovely river," it puffed, "how can I help you?"

"Where did you get them from?" Dart spluttered, trying hard to keep up, "I mean, I'd really like some passengers. Where can I find some?"

The train laughed at Dart and sped up. "Don't you worry," he tooted, "I have a feeling that your passengers are just around the corner."

Dart was excited. Dart rushed on.

The next thing Dart saw was a weir. As he approached it, Dart could see flashes of light and splashes of water. Two salmon were struggling upstream to lay their eggs. They had a long way to go, so Dart curled around them and flicked them up over the weir. The salmon thanked Dart with a wriggle of their tails and swam away.

Dart swirled on.

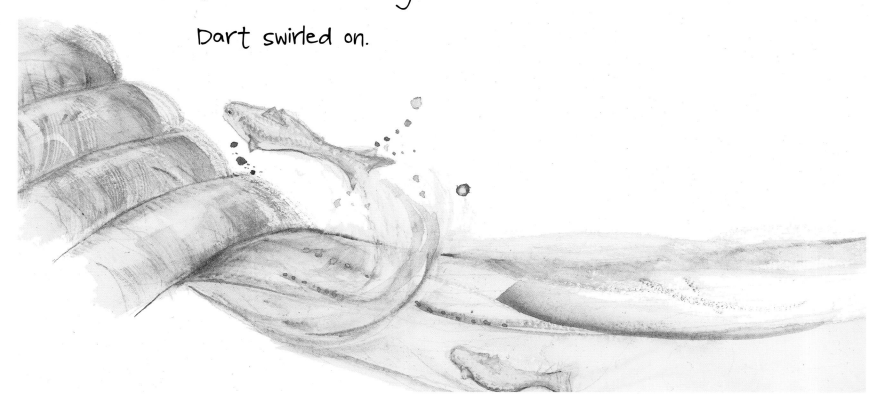

After the weir, everything was quieter,
Dart was deep and wide; he was
a real river now. He flowed under a
large bridge and saw row after row
of boats, each one full of people and
covered in flags. Dart curled himself
around the bow of each boat. The
boats rocked gently and the people
smiled.

Dart flowed past.

Dart the River got wider and wider. He got so wide that little sailing boats could tack backwards and forwards across him. He loved the boats and made pretty shapes around their bows. Dart was getting near to the sea. His water was a bit salty now, and some sea creatures had swept up on the tide. He passed a jetty, where children were trying to catch crabs. They were wrapped up in coats, kicking their feet happily in the water.

Dart swelled on.

Dart reached a harbour. Houses on each bank rose steeply away from him. The harbour was busy with boats crossing from one side to the other. Two stone castles peered at Dart through tiny eye-shaped windows. As Dart rolled past the castles, three little red aeroplanes swooped down and flew back towards the harbour. Waves started to roll in from the sea towards him.

Dart rolled to meet them.

Dart was at the sea. His sweet Dartmoor water mixed with the salty waves. He bobbed around, enjoying the undulating motion. His journey was over. It had been an exciting journey, but he missed Dartmoor. He missed the moor grass, the moss, the wind, the waterfall, the cameras, and the kayakers. What was he supposed to do now? He bobbed for a while longer and thought about it. Eventually an idea came to him.

Dart shouted the idea to the sea and the rocks and the gulls.

All of the locations in 'Dart the River' are real and beautiful. To find them, ask at a local visitor or tourist centre, or use the grid references and the following maps:

For Dartmoor – Ordnance Survey Explorer OL28 (Dartmoor)
For other locations – Ordnance Survey Landranger 202 (Torbay and South Dartmoor)

East Dart Head
(SX 608 855)
Don't get stuck
in a bog!

Postbridge
(SX 648 789)
Take a photo on
the clapper bridge.

Waterfall
(SX 627 810)
Be careful on the
slippery rocks!

Dartmeet
(SX 671 731)
Time for an ice
cream.

Newbridge
(SX 711 708)
How many kayakers can you count?

Dittisham
(SX 867 548)
Has anybody caught a crab?

Staverton Station
(SX 783 637)
Take a ride on a steam train.

Dartmouth Harbour
(SX 879 510)
Take a ride on the Lower Ferry.

Totnes Weir
(SX 800 612)
Can you see the salmon leap?

Dartmouth Castle
(SX 886 502)
Climb to the top of the battlement.

Please be aware; river levels on Dartmoor can rise and fall very quickly. Even shallow water can be dangerous.

Always Respect The Water

Who are the Two Blondes?

The Two Blondes are the co-writers of the popular Dartmoor blog twoblondeswalking.com
They love Dartmoor, their families and Jelly Babies.
They spend much of their spare time teaching and leading young people on Dartmoor and are proud to be involved in both the Ten Tors Challenge and The Duke of Edinburgh's Award.

Blonde One
Likes: Navigating at night, finding old things on Dartmoor and drinking coffee.
Dislikes: Falling in bogs, having to buy new walking boots and being cold.

Blonde Two
Likes: Climbing tors, map reading and eating cake.
Dislikes: Being the slowest up a hill, condensation in her tent and wet feet.